This Book Belongs To:

_____

ABC Tongue Twisters Series
Animal Fun
School Days

Wishing you lots
of giggles!

Joni McCoy

Written by Joni McCoy

Tinlizzy Publishing
ISBN: 978-1-953814-68-5
ABC Tongue Twisters School Days

www.TinlizzyPublishing.com

School Days

Tongue Twisters with things you can find in a school.

Abe the Adorable Ape offered
the Beautiful teacher's assistant,
Betty the Bear, a big red apple.

Betty the beautiful bear
sipped her berry beverage on
this beautiful autumn afternoon.

Aa Bb

Can you count how many words start with the letters A and B?

Benny the Blue beaver placed his blue backpack
on the hook with the help of his bee buddy and
a beautiful blue butterfly.

Below the books, between the banana and the bear.

Bb

Can you count how many words start with the letter B?

Chickie the Colorful chicken created a nest with coloring crayons, under the clock and next to the chalkboard.

Clara brought Chickie to class for show and tell.

Can you count how many words start with the letter C?

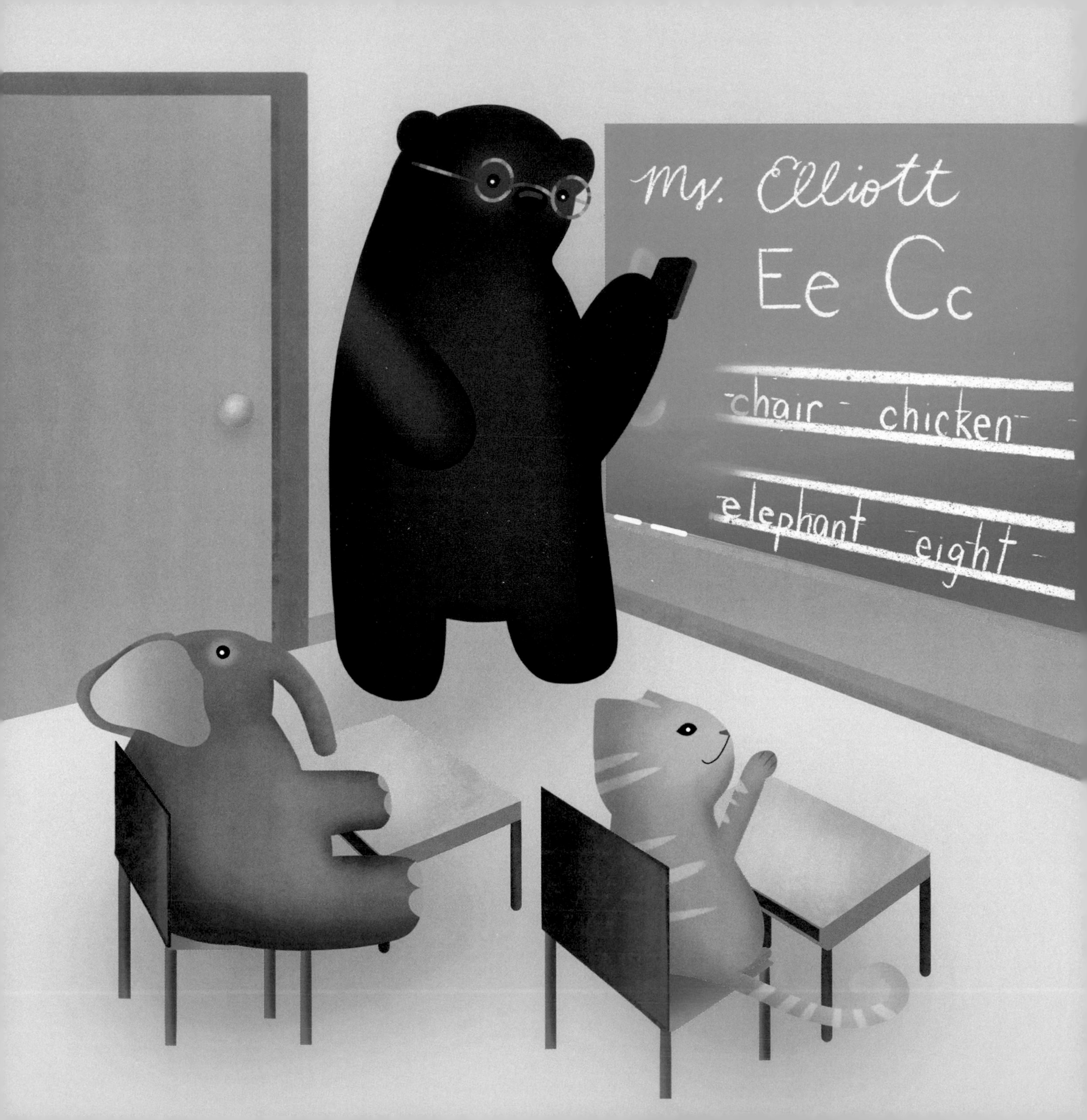
Ms. Elliott
Ee Cc
chair chicken
elephant eight

Mr. Elliott the Educator was erasing the chalkboard
after a lesson on words starting with C and E.
Words like chicken, chair, elephant and eight.

Emma the Elephant and Cindy the Cat were sitting
in their chairs in the classroom, enjoying class.

Cc Ee

Can you count how many words start with the letters C and E?

Dainty Daisy the Purple Spotted Dog sat at her
personal drawing desk.

Penelope the Pretty Parrot perched on Daisy's
shoulder, pausing to praise the pretty pink paint.

Dd Pp

Can you count how many words start with the letters D and P?

Fiona the Fabulous Fox fingerpainted a rainbow
with five colors of fingerpaint.

Freddy the Fidgety Frog leaped forward over the
flashcards his frog friends were flipping.

Can you count how many words start with the letter F?

Gabrielle the Goofy Geicko and Gregory the
Gassy Goat were gazing at all of the green
land on the gigantic globe.

Can you count how many words start with the letter G?

Giselle the Gangly Giraffe glared at Timmy the Tiger
when he tried his technique with the tape and glue.

Gg Tt

Can you count how many words start with the letters G and T?

Lightning lit up the sky as the lunch crowd
lounged in the lunchroom.

Lizzy the Long-Legged Giraffe let her lovely
little classmates lunch on lettuce and lemonade.

Can you count how many words start with the letter L?

Michael the Moody Monkey hung from a map
to see the majestic mountains of Montana.

Mm

Can you count how many words start with the letter M?

Petey the Playful Penguin picked up pencils
with her pretty toes to help the popular
peacock named Patty.

Can you count how many words start with the letter P?

Piper the Practicing Teacher presented percentages on the projector to the pupils.

Piper was pleasantly pleased when her pupil Paige gave her a pretty paperclip necklace.

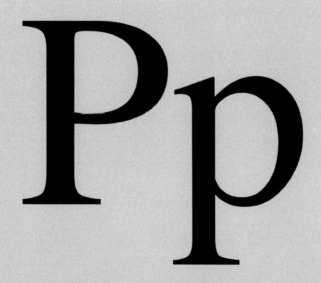

Can you count how many words start with the letter P?

Roman the Rambunctious Raccoon wore his raincoat
on a rainy day.

Roman really respected his rainbow desk and chair.

Rr

Can you count how many words start with the letter R?

Secretly, Sara the Smelly Skunk enjoyed her schoolbooks
as Sam the Sly Sloth slid off his slippery seat.

Ss

Can you count how many words start with the letter S?

Slippery the Slithering Snake skidded to a stop
at the school. Sam the Sly Sloth was stuck on the
roof of the schoolbus, as the bus stopped suddenly.

Ss

Can you count how many words start with the letters S?

Made in the USA
Las Vegas, NV
18 October 2021